The Harcombe Diet®
Lunch box recipes

Quick, easy and nutritious meals for busy people on the go

Published by Columbus Publishing Ltd 2018

www.columbuspublishing.co.uk

ISBN 978-1-907797-45-3

Rev: 20180916

Cover design by Lewis Kokoc

Typesetting by Raffaele Bolelli Gallevi

COLUMBUS PUBLISHING

Contents

Introduction   7

1. About this book   9

2. What you'll need   11

3. Useful notes   15

4. Mains   19

5. Salads   75

6. Sauces & Dips   101

7. What you can eat   119

The Harcombe Diet®
Lunch box recipes

Find out more about Zoë
and/or The Harcombe Diet® at:

www.zoeharcombe.com

www.theharcombediet.com

www.theharcombedietclub.com

Introduction

When we worked in corporate life and travelled extensively we were shocked at the very poor selection of food available to the travelling public, be it motorway service stations, on trains or 'planes.

For the relatively few days that we were office based, lunches were either taken in the works canteen or a quick take-out snack from the local 'deli', which was invariably some baguette based creation containing a few salad leaves and a slice of tomato.

Today, even with the growth in 'healthy options' the general quality of food on offer for the traveller or corporate worker is shockingly poor.

A day out to a business meeting or an overseas trip for a holiday can prove a real challenge for a consumer of real food when it comes to meal times.

The challenge is even greater for those working in offices and factories and becomes even more so for those having to work unsociable shift patterns.

Lunches on the go are still, typically, wheat based produce in the form of a sandwich or pizza with a few green ingredients thrown in to add some colour. They are generally tasteless and do nothing to nourish our bodies through the day.

Unless you are very fortunate to have a works canteen with a proper deli bar or a local restaurant and a decent budget, making your own packed lunch is the only real option for us 'real foodies' who prefer a decent meal while out and about and at work.

While many of us are happy and able to throw together some of last night's chilled leftovers into a tub and take it to work, preparing a delicious set of lunches that make your mouth water when you lift off the lid and then leave you nourished and satisfied for the rest of your working day, takes a bit of planning and organising.

In this handy little book, we'll show you how to do just that.

Chapter 1

About this book

The Harcombe Diet® encourages you to eat as much 'real' food as you need, three times a day. Chapter 7 contain handy reminders of what you can eat in Phase 1 and Phase 2.

Most people reading this book will be familiar with The Harcombe Diet®, so you'll appreciate the "Suitable for" information with each recipe. This will tell you if the recipe is OK for the three conditions, which phase of the diet the recipe is for and whether this is a 'carb' or a 'fat' meal.

For anyone not familiar with the diet, theharcombediet.com site will give you the headlines about the diet, the phases and these all-important conditions, which explain food cravings.

We have tried to include as many Phase 1 options as possible. There are also a lot of fat meals, as we know that it's easier to do brown rice/rice pasta dishes at home. We also know that fat meals are popular among Harcombe followers because we know that fat is our friend!

We've marked vegetarian options (v) on the list of recipes for mains/salads/sauces & dips and in the title for each recipe. A number of the vegetarian options mix real foods (they use seeds and nuts or pulses and cheese, for example). We've included these for two reasons 1) because they are awesome recipes and 2) because we are trying to encourage the mindset that filling up on real food, even with some mixing, is infinitely better than settling for a sandwich with 50 different ingredients.

We work long hours nowadays. Many of you will be having breakfast at 6-7am and not getting home for dinner until 12 hours later. If one great meal in the middle of the day can stop you snacking and having a bad lunch option, the fact that you're mixing is really not a problem.

On this theme, you will find an occasional apricot in a recipe and avocado in a couple. We point out where you can leave things out and where there is a tiny mix (as opposed to a whole recipe mix). Our recommendation is to go with these tiny flexes. The goal is to get you through the day with a super healthy lunch and a wee mix is really not going to hurt.

We've intentionally not included desserts, as you shouldn't need them as part of your lunch box. If you really need something to finish off your meal, have some berries or a square of dark chocolate (at least 70% cocoa and ideally 85% or higher).

The book is structured in three sections:

- Mains

- Salads

- Sauces & Dips

When making your lunchbox for the day, we recommend that you simply add something from each group: a main dish; one, or more salads and a sauce or dip. A perfect Phase 1 combo would be lemon roast chicken with beetroot and watercress salad and herb infused olive oil. Do let us know your favourite combinations in theharcombedietclub. com or on Facebook.

And finally – don't forget the little people! All the recipes in this book are, of course, suitable for children's school lunch boxes too, whatever teacher may say ;-)

Chapter 2

What you'll need

Out and about

You'll need a good range of Tupperware boxes. Most people are likely to have a few in the house already. If not, you'll find everything from half litre to two litre containers handy. Do get a couple of really small ones, under half a litre, as they're great for the sauces and dips. One in the wash and one in use is worth remembering too.

You'll need a set of cutlery that you're happy to carry around with you. Metal is best, but you may also want to have some disposable plastic sets in case you need to take a lunch when you're flying off somewhere.

For the summer months, you may find a small cool bag useful, to keep your food chilled and fresh when you're out and about.

For hot meal options, food flasks are a great invention. If you're someone who prefers hot meals to cold, then invest in a quality food flask. And, of course, they can be used for cold meals too.

At home

We've looked to keep the recipes in this book simple to make and to store, so that you can make them without the need for specialised equipment or ingredients.

In the kitchen you'll need little more than an oven and a blender and a flan tin/baking tray here and there.

There may be a handful of ingredients that need a bit of looking for, but the majority you will be able to find in your local supermarket or grocer, if they are not already in your larder cupboard.

We recommend keeping the following staples at home:

Herbs and spices:
Cayenne pepper, cumin seeds, peppercorns, sea salt, garlic, coriander seeds, mixed herbs, paprika, turmeric, chilli powder.

Larder items:
Olive oil, sesame oil, white wine vinegar, rice flour, almond flour, red/green lentils, balsamic vinegar, Dijon mustard, Harissa paste, Tabasco.

Tinned produce:
Tomatoes, tuna/salmon, kidney beans, chickpeas.

For the fridge:
Bell peppers, mixed lettuce leaves, tomatoes, onions (white and red), Natural Live Yoghurt (NLY), cheddar cheese, butter.

Other staples:
Eggs, mince meat, chicken.

Some preparation time

If you want the quickest and easiest lunch option then just take a tub of salad leaves into work, with some dressing in a separate jar/tub to keep the leaves fresh and then pop some cold meat, a tin of fish or grated cheese on top of the salad at serving time and that's lunch.

This book is about putting in a bit more effort to prepare something really special, so that you feel you've really had a great meal.

We have long encouraged a back-to-baking Sunday. A little time invested in preparing food options on a Sunday, or one evening a week, will transform your lunch options and it can be great fun. All the time we spend watching cookery programmes, we could be doing it ourselves!

Our weekday lunches will, mainly, be a mixture of three or four groups of pre-prepared ingredients and it's these groups of ingredients that will need preparing in advance.

Other recipes will involve pre-cooking, or part-cooking, and chilling or freezing so that a suitable meal portion can be quickly packed and taken to work with you.

Of course, the recipes are not limited to work lunches only. They can form the perfect basis for snacks, picnics or even a quick and easy meal at home. They're also great for an 'as-you-like-it' meal, an ensemble of various dishes laid out on a table for you to enjoy as you please. If you have children, they'll love 'as-you-like-it' meals and you may be surprised at how much even the pickiest of eaters will eat when they have a range of delicious, colourful and healthy foods to select from, especially if you let them eat with their fingers!

For a typical week, where two adults need five lunchboxes, we estimate that the preparation time need be no more than a couple of hours. You'll reduce this further with practice and you can always save time by having a main dish for an evening meal, which you can then use in your lunchbox for the next couple of days. For example, go for a slightly larger than usual pork joint for a slow roast one evening and you'll have leftovers for lunches for the next couple of days.

As with everything in life - you'll get out of this what put in and we so hope that you enjoy the putting in as much as the getting out and feel encouraged to start and maintain a great lunch box habit.

Chapter 3

Useful notes

When we list weights or volumes for ingredients, these are always pre-cooked weights and volumes. Hence "100g brown rice" on the ingredients list will be 100g of brown rice grains straight from the packet – the weight will approximately double when cooked for this particular ingredient. 200g of spinach, on the contrary, will reduce in weight a little and substantially in volume, when it is cooked.

Most recipes are designed to serve four people. Please adjust the quantities to suit your family size and/or to make some leftovers for another meal.

To make the recipes easy to follow, we have listed all the ingredients in the order that you will use them.

Many of our recipes refer to a large frying pan. This can be a wok – whatever you normally use to fry things with minimal olive oil.

If there is anything you don't like in a recipe, leave it out or swap it for something similar (one spice for another, one vegetable for another etc). Recipes are meant to be adapted to suit your tastes.

Please check any tins or packets for unnecessary ingredients. You'll find sugar in tins of vegetables and pulses unless you're careful. Tins of tomatoes usually have citric acid as an added ingredient – this is fine as a preservative. Stock cubes are virtually impossible to get without sugar (an 'ose') somewhere on the list. Get one with any nasties as far down the list as possible and then don't worry. The cube is usually about a centimetre squared and it ends up being added to a lot of liquid in a dish serving four people, so the amount you end up with is absolutely minute.

Tinned vegetables are fine. Tinned fish is especially healthy, if you choose the options with bones and skin left in - that's where the vitamin D is most concentrated. Frozen vegetables are also fine as an alternative to fresh vegetables and useful to keep in stock.

We always recommend Natural Live Yoghurt (also called bio on some labels) and this is important for Phase 1. For Phase 2 recipes, it's OK to use normal yoghurt, if you can't get live yoghurt.

Weights, measures & temperatures

We've used the metric system for weights and temperatures and have also included an imperial conversion where appropriate.

We list Fahrenheit, Celsius and gas marks on every recipe to make sure that the setting for your own oven is always to hand, without the need to convert.

For completeness, here is a useful reminder of the various conversions that you may need while using this book.

Oven temperature conversions

Fahrenheit	Centigrade	Gas Mark	Description
225 – 275 f	110 – 135 c	0 – 1	Very Cool
300 – 325 f	150 – 165 c	2 – 3	Cool
350 – 375 f	175 – 190 c	4 – 5	Moderate
400 – 425 f	200 – 220 c	6 – 7	Hot
450 – 475 f	230 – 245 c	8 – 9	Very Hot

Conversion table for weight: Metric to imperial

Metric (g)	Metric (Kg)	Imperial (Oz)	Imperial (Lbs)
100	0.1	3.5	0.22
250	0.25	8.75	0.55
500	0.5	17.5	1.1
1000	1	35	2.2

Conversion table for volumes and liquids

USA (Cups)	Universal (Tablespoons)	Imperial (Fluid oz)	Imperial (Pints)	Metric (Ml)	Other
1/16	1	–	–	15	= 3 teasp
1/8	2	1	–	30	–
¼	4	2	1/8	60	–
½	8	4	¼	120	–
¾	12	6	1/6	175	–
1	16	8	½	240	–
2	32	16	1	480	–
4.2	68	34	2.1	1000	= 1 litre

Chapter 4

Mains

This is the 'meaty' chapter, where we look at the delicious recipes that you can be enjoying for your packed lunch as soon as tomorrow (depending on what you have in your fridge right now).

There is no fixed portion size for each main item and you should adjust the quantities to suit what you need to get you through your busy day and to your next complete meal.

We all get times when our blood sugar gets a bit low, we get the shakes and we reach for a snack. Having some healthy snacks available in your fridge or lunchbox helps to make sure that you make good choices for your health, rather than succumbing to a sugar laden cereal bar or bar of confectionery.

Like all the recipes in this book, these dishes can be made in advance and will usually keep for five days or more in a fridge (depending on the original freshness of ingredients).

In this chapter:

- *Chicken – Roast, lemon & garlic, herb crusted, mustard, chilli roast*
- *Chicken breast stuffed with Guacamole*
- *Bacon wrapped chicken*
- *Tandoori chicken*
- *Cheese topped chicken breast*

- Cajun seasoning (For chicken, pork, beef, bacon, fish etc.)
- Coronation chicken wrap
- Kebabs – Pork, chicken or beef
- Chicken burgers
- Slow roast pork
- Scotch eggs
- Mustard roast ham
- Zingy fish patties
- Harissa spiced Koftas
- Chilli prawns
- Meatzas
- Meatza Toppings – Quattro Stagioni, Margherita, Tex-Mex
- Lunchbox 'Eggza' (v)
- Homemade pâté
- Chicken liver parfait
- Loaded bacon strips (guacamole/salsa)
- Cheese & bacon muffins
- Egg mayonnaise (v)
- Frittata (v)
- Omelette strips (v)
- Oopsies (v)
- Spicy chick pea patties (v)
- Wheat free flans (v) – Courgette, pepper & Mozzarella, Roasted tomato & Feta, Asparagus & Cheddar cheese
- Lentil & buckwheat biscuits (v)
- Lentil & cheese slab (v)
- Carrot, parsnip, celeriac & mixed seed bake (v)
- Chewy fruit bars (v)
- Nut Roast (v)

(v) = vegetarian

Roast Chicken

Ingredients	Suitable for
1 chicken	Phase 1 & 2 (fat)
Serves	Candida
4	Hypoglycemia
	Wheat free
	Dairy free

Poulet roti was always one of Andy's favourite meals during the years he lived in France. The moist texture of a slow roast bird, coupled with its deliciously crispy skin, was always a feast to look forward to. And, of course, any leftovers were always a welcome addition to the next day's lunchbox.

We're suggesting a couple of options to the basic roast chicken and, if you follow the same cooking method for them all, you'll end up with the same delicious 'roti'.

Basic method

1 Pre heat the oven 180° C / 350° F / Gas 4.

2 Place the chicken breast side down in a roasting dish and pop in the oven for 30 minutes. This will allow juices to flow into the breast meat, making it lovely and moist.

3 Remove from the oven and carefully turn the bird over, taking care not to puncture the skin. Pop back in the oven and roast for a further 30 minutes.

4 Turn the oven temperature up to 200° C / 400° F / Gas 6 and roast for a further 30 minutes until the skin is a nice crispy brown and the juices run clear.

Lemon and Garlic Roast Chicken

Ingredients	Suitable for
1 chicken	Phase 1 & 2 (fat)
2 cloves garlic, peeled	Candida
1 lemon, cut in quarters	Hypoglycemia
Serves	Wheat free
4	Dairy free

Method

1 Put the garlic cloves into the chicken and then squeeze the juice of the lemon into the chicken. Pop the remaining wedges in too.

2 Cook as per the basic method.

Herb Crusted Chicken

Ingredients	Suitable for
1 chicken	Phase 1 & 2 (fat)
1 onion, peeled and quartered	Candida
2 tablespoons olive oil	Hypoglycemia
2 teaspoons dried mixed herbs	Wheat free
Serves	Dairy free
4	

Method

1 Put the onion into the chicken.

2 Rub the olive oil onto the chicken skin and then sprinkle the mixed herbs all over the skin (the olive oil will help the herbs to stick).

3 Cook as per the basic method.

Mustard Roast Chicken

Ingredients	Suitable for
1 chicken	Phase 2 (fat)
1 onion, peeled and quartered	Candida
2 teaspoons Dijon mustard	Hypoglycemia
Serves	Wheat free
4	Dairy free

Strictly speaking we don't allow mustard in Phase 1, but you have to try this to believe how much difference a scraping of mustard can make to a chicken. You can save this recipe until Phase 2. Or have it in Phase 1 and give the skin (the mustard in effect) to someone else. Or be chilled about the fact that half a teaspoon of mustard (your share in the recipe) will make so little difference that the taste is worth it.

Method

1 Put the onion into the chicken.

2 Spoon the mustard over the chicken and, using the back of the spoon, make sure that the breast, legs and wings are evenly covered.

3 Cook as per the basic method.

Chilli Roast Chicken

Ingredients	Suitable for
1 chicken	Phase 1 & 2 (fat)
2 tablespoons olive oil	Candida
2 teaspoons chilli flakes	Hypoglycemia
Serves	Wheat free
4	Dairy free

Method

1 Rub the olive oil into the chicken skin and then sprinkle the chilli flakes all over the skin.

2 Cook as per the basic method.

Chicken breast stuffed with Guacamole

Ingredients	Suitable for
4 chicken breasts	Phase 2/3 (fat)
4 tablespoons guacamole (p. 112)	Candida
Serves	Hypoglycemia
4	Wheat free
	Dairy free

Not only does this dish look exotic, it tastes it too. No one, yourself included, will believe you knocked it up in 15 minutes.

Method

1 Place the chicken breast skin side down on a tray and grill for 5 minutes. Turn the breast over and grill for a further 5 minutes until cooked through and the skin turns brown and crispy. Put aside to cool.

2 When cool, slice along the length of the breast to open up a pouch, into which you can stuff the guacamole.

3 Chill and use as required.

Bacon wrapped chicken

Ingredients	Suitable for
4 chicken breasts	Phase 1 & 2 (fat)
4 large bacon rashers	Candida
Serves	Hypoglycemia
4	Wheat free
	Dairy free

This is a really simple way to spruce up a chicken breast, and it just takes 15 minutes to prepare and cook. It's delicious with our raw tomato salsa (p. 102).

Method

1 Take a chicken breast and tightly wrap a bacon rasher around it. Pierce with a cocktail stick to hold in place. Repeat for the other 3 breasts.

2 Place the chicken pieces on a tray and grill for 5 minutes. Turn the breasts over and grill for a further 5 minutes until cooked through and until the bacon fat is nice and crispy.

3 Chill and use as required.

Tandoori Chicken

Ingredients

4 chicken pieces

200g (7oz) Greek style Natural Live Yoghurt

3 teaspoons tandoori spice mix (1 teaspoon each of ground ginger, ground cumin, ground coriander, paprika, turmeric, salt, cayenne pepper)

Sea salt and freshly ground pepper

Suitable for

Phase 1 & 2 (fat)

Candida

Hypoglycemia

Wheat free

Serves

4

Method

1 Pre-heat the oven to 200° C, 400° F, Gas 6.

2 Slash the chicken pieces and place them on a shallow dish.

3 Thouroughly mix the yoghurt, spices, salt and pepper and pour over the chicken pieces, turning the chicken pieces so that they are well covered. Cover with cling film, chill and leave for at least 8 hrs.

4 Pop the chicken in the oven and roast for about 30 minutes until the chicken is cooked through.

5 Chill and use as required.

Cheese topped chicken breast

Ingredients	Suitable for
4 chicken breasts	Phase 2 (fat)
50g (2oz) grated cheddar	Candida
(or similar hard cheese)	Hypoglycemia
Serves	Wheat free
4	

This recipe uses chicken as a base for a classic dish (rather than toast). Like the bacon wrapped chicken, this is delicious with our raw tomato salsa (p. 102).

Method

1 Take a chicken breast and slice it along its length, leaving just enough meat to hold it together as a single breast. Place it on a chopping board and lightly bash it with your fist until flat. Repeat for the other breasts.

2 Place the chicken pieces on a tray and grill for 5 minutes. Turn the breasts over and grill for a further 2 minutes, until cooked through.

3 Remove from the grill and sprinkle each breast with some of the grated cheese, using about a quarter on each breast. Pop back under the grill for a further 3-5 minutes until the cheese is bubbling and starting to brown.

4 Chill and use as required.

Cajun seasoning
(for chicken, pork, beef, bacon, fish etc.)

Ingredients	Suitable for
½ teaspoon cardamom seeds	Phase 1 & 2 (can accompany a carb/fat meal)
1 teaspoon coriander seeds	
1 teaspoon cumin seeds	Candida
1 teaspoon fennel seeds	Hypoglycemia
1 teaspoon black peppercorns	Wheat free
2 teaspoons dried oregano	Dairy free
1 teaspoon dried basil	**Serves**
1 teaspoon paprika	4
½ teaspoon chilli powder	
½ teaspoon garlic salt	

This is an all time favourite for so many people. The seasoning can be rubbed on just about anything you like and it's particularly delicious for grilled and barbcue'd food. We make big batches and keep the seasoning in a herb jar for everyday use.

Method

1 Put the cardamom, coriander, cumin and fennel seeds together with the black peppercorns in a pestle and mortar and crush them well.

2 Transfer the crushed seeds and peppercorns to a mixing bowl and add the remaining ingredients. Mix everything together thoroughly.

3 Rub the mixture into steak, lamb, pork, chicken, fish, aubergine steaks, vegetables and anything else that you would barbecue or grill. Cook the meat, fish or vegetables as you would normally.

Coronation chicken wrap

Ingredients

75g (2.5oz) full fat, Natural Live Yoghurt (Greek style)

1 teaspoon of Dijon mustard

2 dried apricots, chopped (optional)

100g (4oz) precooked chicken (you can use the scrapings off the carcase for this)

Sea salt and freshly ground pepper

2 iceberg lettuce leaves per serving

Suitable for

Phase 2 (fat)

Candida

Hypoglycemia

Wheat free

Serves

1

This is a great way to use up any bits of left over chicken, as the appearance of the meat is disguised when it's mixed up with the other ingredients. It's also surprisingly rich and filling.

Method

1 In a mixing bowl, thoroughly mix the yoghurt, mustard, apricots and chicken and then season with salt and pepper.

2 Take 2 iceberg lettuce leaves and place one inside the other to create a small dish and spoon the mixture into the middle. Then, wrap the lettuce leaves around the chicken and yoghurt mixture and eat with your hands.

TIP *You can leave out the apricots to be strict or just pop a small single dried apricot in the dish. It adds more in taste and texture than it adds in carb content. The Mustard roast chicken recipe on p. 24, can help with any mustard queries.*

Kebabs – pork, chicken or Beef

Ingredients

450g (1lb) meat, diced (pork, chicken, beef or a mixture)

4 tablespoons olive oil

2 tablespoon lemon juice

½ teaspoon cumin powder

½ teaspoon cardamom powder

½ teaspoon garam masala

½ teaspoon chilli powder

2 cloves garlic, crushed

1 red & 1 yellow pepper, deseeded and chopped into 2-3 cm squares

(barbecue skewers)

Suitable for

Phase 1 & 2 (fat)

Candida

Hypoglycemia

Wheat free

Dairy free

Serves

4

Method

1 Cut the meat into 2-3cm cubes.

2 Mix the oil, lemon juice, spices and garlic.

3 Pour the mixture over the meat, cover and marinate for 60-90 minutes.

4 Alternate the pepper squares with the meat cubes as you slide them onto the skewers.

5 Grill, or barbecue under a high flame, for 10 minutes.

Chicken burgers

Ingredients

4 chicken breasts, sliced in half
lengthways

8 bacon rashers

2 medium tomatoes, sliced

½ red onion, finely sliced

4 tablespoons Natural Live Yoghurt
(NLY) or mayonnaise (p. 107)

Sea salt and freshly ground pepper

Suitable for

Phase 1 (can be) & Phase 2 (fat)

Candida (NLY option)

Hypoglycemia

Wheat free

Dairy free (mayo option)

Serves

4

This recipe is not what the name suggests. Rather than using ground chicken to make a burger, we'll be using chicken breasts as a replacement for the traditional burger bun.

Method

1 Heat a griddle pan and cook the chicken breast slices for about 5 minutes on each side.

2 While the chicken is cooking, fry or grill the bacon until crispy and prepare the other ingredients.

3 To make the burgers, place a chicken slice on a plate and then build up a layer of NLY/mayonnaise, bacon, tomato and onion and repeat. Season with salt and pepper and top off with another chicken slice.

TIP 1 *To make these burgers even more filling, try adding a layer of grated cheese or guacamole instead of the NLY/ mayonnaise (this would then make it a Phase 2/3 dish).*

TIP 2 *Natural Live Yoghurt, rather than mayonnaise, makes this OK for Phase 1 and Candida.*

Slow roast pork

Ingredients	Suitable for
1kg (2lb) rolled shoulder of pork	Phase 1 & 2 (fat)
1 onion, peeled and sliced into rings	Candida
Serves	Hypoglycemia
4-6	Wheat free
	Dairy free

Slow roast pork is not only delicious hot, it is also a perfect base for a lunch box meal. If you can resist eating all the crackling hot, then it also adds an interesting texture to your cold meal. Keep some apple sauce back too and spoon a dollop on top of the cold pork.

Method

1 Place the onion rings on a piece of aluminium foil large enough to cover the pork and then place the pork on top of the onions. Wrap the foil around the meat, making sure that it's sealed to keep all the juices in. Cook in a cool oven 135° C, 275° F, Gas 1 for at least 6 hours.

2 Remove from the oven, carefully unwrap the meat and slice off the skin. Re-wrap the joint and leave to stand in a warm place.

3 Put the skin on a tray and pop under a medium grill to crispen. This will take about 10-15 minutes. Resist the temptation to cook it too fast as it will just burn and be ruined.

4 Carve the meat and enjoy hot and chill what remains for your lunch box, carving as required.

Scotch eggs

Ingredients	Suitable for
450g (1lb) minced beef	Phase 1 & 2 (fat)
1 onion, finely chopped	Candida
1 clove garlic, crushed	Hypoglycemia
3 teaspoons dried mixed herbs	Wheat free
Few dashes Tabasco	Dairy free
Sea salt and freshly ground pepper	**Serves***
4 small chicken eggs, hard boiled (8 minutes) and shelled	4

*Note: these are quite dense and filling so you may only need ½ of a Scotch egg per lunchbox – especially if you're adding salad and dip selections

These are traditionally rolled in breadcrumbs to help hold them together but, with a little care, you can make them wheat free and you lose none of the taste.

Method

1 Pre-heat the oven to 200° C, 400° F, Gas 6.

2 Put the minced beef, onion, garlic, herbs, Tabasco, salt and pepper in a mixing bowl and thoroughly mix together.

3 Take a quarter of the mixture and form a thin burger shape. Place a boiled egg onto the mixture and gently fold the minced meat mixture around the egg, pressing firmly so that it holds its shape. Place on a roasting tray and repeat for the other 3 eggs.

4 Pop in the oven and cook for about 40 minutes, until the meat browns. Remove from the oven to cool.

5 Chill and serve as required.

Mustard roast ham

Ingredients	Suitable for
1kg (2lb) ham or gammon joint	Phase 1 (can be) & Phase 2 (fat)
2 teaspoons Dijon mustard	Candida
Serves	Hypoglycemia
4-6	Wheat free
	Dairy free

Much of the ham that you can buy in supermarkets is preserved with water and sugar, so why not cook your own? It takes little-to-no effort and tastes so good.

Method

1 Spoon the mustard over the ham joint, making sure that it's well covered. Place it on some aluminium foil, large enough to cover the whole joint. Wrap the foil around the meat, making sure that it's sealed to keep all the juices in. Cook in a medium oven, 175° C, 350° F , Gas 4, for about 2 hours.

2 Remove from the oven, open up the foil to expose the meat and return to the oven. Increase the heat to 200° C, 400° F, Gas 6 and roast for a further 30 minutes.

3 Remove from the oven, again, and recover the meat with the foil to rest for about half an hour.

4 Transfer the meat to a dish and chill. Use as required.

TIP *See the mustard roast chicken recipe on p. 24 for some thoughts on mustard. Mustard can't be left out of this recipe but you could easily go for the middle cuts from the joint for a Phase 1 meal (avoid the mustard brushed outer layer).*

Zingy fish patties

Ingredients

450g (1lb) white fish flaked (cod, hake, Pollack etc will all do)

Juice of half a lemon

1 chilli, deseeded and finely chopped

2 eggs

Freshly ground pepper

Knob of butter for frying

Suitable for

Phase 1 & 2 (fat)

Candida

Hypoglycemia

Wheat free

Serves

4

Method

1 Put the fish, lemon juice and chilli in a mixing bowl and mix together. Leave to stand for 15 minutes for the flavours to infuse.

2 Beat the eggs and add to the bowl. Mix thoroughly until you have a messy looking fish paste, then mix in some freshly ground pepper.

3 Take palm-sized amounts of the paste and mould in your hands to create small fish patties. You should be able to make about 8-10 of them.

4 Heat the butter in a frying pan and gently add the patties. Cook for 3-4 minutes on each side until they are nicely browned.

5 Chill and enjoyed as a snack or add to a lunchbox with your favourite salad and relish.

Harissa spiced koftas

Ingredients	Suitable for
450g (1lb) mince lamb	Phase 1 & 2 (fat)
1 small onion, finely chopped	Candida
2 teaspoons Harissa paste	Hypoglycemia
Sea salt and freshly ground pepper	Wheat free
(barbecue skewers)	Dairy free
Serves	
4	

Method

1 Place the lamb, onion and Harissa paste in a mixing bowl and mix thoroughly. Season well with sea salt and freshly ground pepper.

2 Take a small handful of the paste and mould over a wooden skewer, repeat for 7 other skewers, making 8 Koftas. Alternatively, make 8-10 small meatballs.

3 Either fry, grill, roast or barbq the Koftas/meatballs for about 10 minutes (5 mins each side for Koftas or 15 minutes for meatballs).

TIP *Try these with some of the yoghurt dips in the Sauces & Dips section.*

Chilli prawns

Ingredients

2 tablespoons olive oil

2 chillies, deseeded & chopped
(more if you like food really spicy)

2 cloves of garlic, finely sliced

16 large prawns

Juice of 1 lemon

Suitable for

Phase 1 & 2 (fat)

Candida

Hypoglycemia

Wheat free

Dairy free

Serves

4

Method

1 Heat the olive oil in a frying pan and, when the oil is hot, add the chillies and garlic and fry for 1 minute.

2 Add the prawns and fry for a further 4-5 minutes, turning regularly, until the prawn shells are lightly burnt.

3 Transfer the prawns to a warmed dish and pour the oil from the frying pan over the prawns.

4 Squeeze the juice of the lemon over the prawns, then chill and use as required as a lunch box main or a tasty snack on their own.

TIP *You can use pre-cooked prawns as an option.*

Meatzas

Ingredients	Suitable for
For the base:	Phase 1* & 2 (fat)
450g (1lb) mince beef	Candida
Olive oil for cooking	Hypoglycemia
1 large onion, very finely chopped	Wheat free
1 clove garlic, crushed	Dairy free*
1 egg	**Serves**
1 teaspoon dried oregano	4-6
1 teaspoon dried basil	** Once you add cheese to your toppings, you're no longer Phase 1 and dairy free*
½ teaspoon dried fennel	
Sea salt and freshly ground pepper	

If you've previously enjoyed delicious, thin crust pizzas, laden with bubbling melted cheese, herbs, peppers and tomatoes but now abstain from wheat, you should try a Meatza.

Meatzas basically replace the floury pizza base with a delicious ground meat base, which can be jazzed up with onions, herbs and spices. Top them off with your favourite pizza topping and you have a very tasty, and nutritious, pizza alternative.

You can cook up a Meatza for an evening meal and then chill what's left for use in your lunchbox over the next couple of days. Once cooked, it will keep for up to 5 days in your fridge.

Here's our basic recipe, which you can adapt to suit your own preferences.

Method

1 Pre-heat the oven to 200° C, 400° F, Gas 6.

2 Gently fry the onion and garlic in a generous amount of olive oil. Do this very

slowly - they should be lightly caramelised when done.

3 In a mixing bowl, add the minced meat, fried onion, herbs and egg and mix thoroughly. Then, pat into the base of a baking dish so that the whole base is covered.

4 Cook in the oven for 20-30 mins until the mixture is a dark brown.

5 Pour off some of the excess fat from the baked base and allow to cool for about 10 minutes.

6 For the simplest of toppings, cover with cheese, peppers, tomatoes and any other ingredients that you fancy and place back in the oven. Cook for a further 15 minutes until the cheese is bubbling. For other toppings, we have some suggestions on the following pages.

Base variations

Try different minced meats, like chicken, pork, turkey or lamb and different herbs and spice combinations. For example, Lamb with Rosemary or Oregano; Turkey with oregano and cumin; or a mixed beef and pork mince with onion and garlic.

Meatza toppings

Quattro stagioni

Ingredients

200g (7oz) of tinned tomatoes (chopped)

4 artichoke hearts (tinned are fine)

Handful of black olives

150g (5oz) sliced mushrooms

50g (2oz) finely chopped ham

1 Mozzarella (approx. 100g (3.5oz))

Drizzle of olive oil

Method

1 Spread the chopped tomatoes over the meatza base.

2 Arrange the other four toppings (artichoke hearts, olives, mushrooms, ham), along with some Mozzarella in each of the four quarters of the meatza base.

3 Drizzle some olive oil over the topping and pop under a hot grill for about 10 minutes until the Mozzarella is bubbling.

4 This is perfect chilled for your lunchbox with one or two of the salads.

Margherita

Ingredients

200g (7oz) of tinned tomatoes (chopped)

1 clove garlic, finely chopped

300g (10.5oz) Mozzarella, chopped into small chunks

100g (3.5oz) grated Parmesan or Pecorino

Handful of fresh basil leaves, cut into strips

2 tablespoons olive oil

Method

1 Spread the chopped tomatoes over the Meatza base.

2 Arrange the remaining ingredients evenly over the base of your Meatza

3 Drizzle some olive oil over the topping and pop under a hot grill for about 10 minutes until the cheese melts.

4 This is perfect chilled for your lunchbox with one or two of the salads.

Tex-Mex

Ingredients

200g (7oz) of tinned tomatoes (chopped)

100g (3.5oz) cheddar cheese, grated

2 tablespoons grated Parmesan cheese

1 teaspoon chopped jalapeno pepper

4 spring onions, chopped

2 cloves garlic, minced

1 avocado, chopped

100g (3.5oz) sour cream

2 tablespoons chopped fresh coriander

Method

1 Spread the chopped tomatoes over the meatza base.

2 Mix the grated cheddar and Parmesan together and then sprinkle over the tomatoes.

3 Sprinkle the peppers, onions, garlic and avocado evenly on top of the cheese and then place under a hot grill until the cheese is bubbling.

4 Remove from the grill and spoon the sour cream on top.

5 Sprinkle with coriander and serve.

TIP *You can leave out the avocado if you don't want to mix at all, but this is still pretty much a fat meal.*

Lunchbox 'Eggza' (v)

Ingredients	Suitable for
Basic 'Eggza' Base:	Phase 2 (fat)
4 eggs	Candida
1½ tablespoons almond flour	Hypoglycemia
50g (2oz) grated Parmesan, or other	Wheat free
hard cheese alternative	**Serves**
Sea salt and freshly ground pepper	2
Butter for frying	

Our lunchbox Eggza is our meat-free alternative to our Meatza base, which will allow you to enjoy all your regular 'pizza' favourites using the humble egg. The bases are quick and easy to make and you can then add your favourite 'pizza' toppings.

Method

1 Whisk the eggs in a mixing bowl and then stir in all the other ingredients.

2 Melt the butter in a frying pan and pour in the mixture, making sure the pan is evenly covered. Cook on a low heat for about 15-20 minutes until the mixture is set.

3 Turn out onto a baking dish and create your favourite topping. If the topping needs cooking, pop it under the grill for a few minutes.

TIP *For the carb conscious, almond flour has about 1.5g of carbohydrate per tablespoon, so you've only got a couple of grams of carbohydrate in this whole recipe.*

Homemade pâté

Ingredients	Suitable for
1 teaspoon butter	Phase 2 (fat)
1 large onion, chopped	Candida
450g (1lb) lambs liver, chopped	Hypoglycemia
2 bacon rashers, chopped	Wheat free
Butter for cooking	**Serves**
Salt & pepper – plenty	4
½ teaspoon dried Italian herbs	
50g (2oz) double cream	

Liver is one of nature's super foods but many people unfortunately find the texture unpalatable. Pâté, therefore, is a great way to get healthy liver into your diet in a delicious dish. Once made, the pâté should keep for a week in a cold fridge and you can eat it as a snack (delicious on celery), with a salad and one guest even had it for breakfast with their bacon and egg!

Method

1 Heat the butter in a frying pan and lightly fry the onion. Set it aside.

2 Fry the liver & bacon in this pan until browned.

3 Return the onions to the pan and stir well together. Add the salt & pepper and the herbs.

4 Put the mixture in a mixing bowl and cool for 10 minutes.

5 Add the cream and hand blend until the substance forms a coarse paste.

6 Place the pâté in small pots, or one serving dish, as desired.

7 Add a knob of butter to the frying pan and a good pinch of herbs. Melt and pour on top of the pâté for an authentic and delicious finish.

Chicken liver parfait

Ingredients	Suitable for
1 teaspoon butter	Phase 1 (can be) & Phase 2 (fat)
½ onion, finely chopped	Candida
1 clove garlic, crushed	Hypoglycemia
250g (9oz) chicken livers	Wheat free
½ teaspoon dried thyme	**Serves**
2 tablespoons brandy (optional)	4
50g (2oz) butter	

This is another pâté recipe that is so easy to make. You can whizz it up in 15 minutes and enjoy it for the rest of the week.

Method

1 Heat the butter in a frying pan and lightly fry the onion and garlic. Transfer the onion and garlic to a mixing bowl and then quickly fry the chicken livers in the same pan. Turn the livers frequently and cook for about 5-6 minutes. Do not overcook - the livers should still be pink inside.

2 Add the livers to the onion and garlic and add the thyme, brandy and butter. With a hand blender, blend the mixture until you have a smooth paste. Then spoon it into a suitably sized pot/bowl.

3 Melt a little butter, about 10g/ ½ oz in the frying pan and pour over the parfait in the pot (there's no need to heat the pan, there should be enough residual heat to melt the butter).

TIP *The brandy is for the dinner party version and connoisseurs. Leave it out for Phase 1.*

Loaded bacon strips

Ingredients	Suitable for
8 slices bacon	Phase 1 (with just the salsa) & Phase
Homemade Guacamole (p. 112)	2/3 (with the Guacamole) (fat)
Homemade tomato salsa (p. 102)	Candida
Freshly ground black pepper	Hypoglycemia
Serves	Wheat free
4	Dairy free

Bacon isn't just for breakfast. These loaded bacon strips are delicious served as the main part of a lunchbox or as a healthy and tasty snack to keep in the fridge, just in case.

Method

1 Grill the bacon under a hot grill for 3-4 minutes each side, until the fat is nicely browned. Transfer to a plate to cool.

2 Spoon the Guacamole onto the bacon strips, pressing it down slightly so that it stays in place.

3 Spoon some homemade salsa on top and finish with some freshly ground pepper.

TIP *You can load with just salsa if you don't want to mix at all, but this is still pretty much a fat meal.*

Cheese & bacon muffins

Ingredients	Suitable for
Makes 12 cups:	Phase 1 (can be) & Phase 2 (fat)
12 slices bacon	Candida
8 eggs	Hypoglycemia
50g (2oz) grated cheddar cheese	Wheat free
pinch of salt	Dairy free (can be)
freshly ground black pepper	**Serves**
	6

Method

1 Preheat oven to 175° C, 350° F, Gas 4.

2 Lightly coat a tray with 12 muffin holes with a little olive oil (or use a 6 hole tray for larger cups). Wrap each piece of bacon inside each muffin cup.

3 Whip the eggs, salt, pepper and cheese with a fork and fill each bacon lined muffin cup ¾ of the way with the egg mixture.

4 Bake for 30-35 minutes, until the egg cups are golden brown and don't jiggle. Use a knife to scoop them out of the tins.

5 Allow to cool and serve with one of your favourite salad options.

6 For a variant, mix in some finely chopped red pepper with the eggs in step 3.

TIP *Leave out the cheese for Phase 1/dairy free bacon & egg muffins.*

Egg mayonnaise (v)

Ingredients	Suitable for
4 tablespoons Natural Live Yoghurt	Phase 2 (fat)
1 teaspoon Dijon mustard	Candida
Salt and freshly ground pepper	Hypoglycemia
4 eggs, hardboiled	Wheat free
	Serves
	4

This is another classic dish, made 'Harcombe friendly' by swapping out a few ingredients. We suggest you batch cook the eggs and then make the 'mayo' fresh as required.

Method

1 Mix the yoghurt, mustard, salt and pepper in a bowl.

2 Peel the eggs and roughly chop them into the bowl with the yoghurt mix.

3 Give the whole lot a good stir with a fork and then use as required.

Frittata (v)

Ingredients	Suitable for
Large knob of butter	Phase 2 (fat)
1 large red pepper, diced	Candida (if no mushrooms)
50g (2oz) fresh spinach	Hypoglycemia
6 eggs	Wheat free
100g (3.5oz) feta cheese	**Serves**
Some freshly ground black pepper	4

Frittata's are an endlessly versatile dish that are equally as delicious as a snack or a main dish for a meal. You can serve them warm or cold and they are a perfect pre-prepare option for lunchboxes.

Method

1 Melt the butter in a heavy frying pan and lightly fry the diced pepper for about a minute, then cover with the fresh spinach.

2 Whisk the eggs and pour them over the spinach. Cook on a low heat for about 5 minutes and then crumble the feta cheese into the mixture. Cook for a further 15 minutes, or until the whole mixture is set.

3 Turn out (upside down) onto a large plate so that the nicely brown underside is facing up.

4 Serve a slice immediately and/or chill for the lunch box.

5 Options: Try broccoli and tuna; cheese and mushroom; cheese and tomato; bacon and onion, for starters.

Omelette strips (v)

Ingredients	Suitable for
Large knob of butter	Phase 1 & 2 (fat)
Handful of any leftover meat or veg (e.g. chicken, beef, broccoli, cauliflower, beans, onions etc.)	Candida
	Hypoglycemia
	Wheat free
4 eggs	**Serves**
Salt and freshly ground pepper	2

This is a great way to use up any leftover meat or veg that may be in your fridge while providing a delicious lunch option that you can toss into your lunchbox. It's basically an omelette, which you allow to cool and then slice up into strips to top your salad with.

Method

1 Lightly fry the leftovers in the butter for 3-5 minutes until warmed through.

2 Break the eggs into a bowl, give them a good whisk with a fork, season with salt and pepper then pour them into the frying pan.

3 Cook for a further 5 minutes, stirring occasionally during the first minute until the whole mixture is cooked through then fold out onto a plate and leave to cool.

4 Chill in a fridge until required then slice into 2cm wide strips to top your salad.

Oopsies (v)

Ingredients	Suitable for
3 eggs	*Phase 2 (fat)*
A generous pinch of sea salt	*Candida*
100g (3.5oz) cream cheese	*Hypoglycemia*
½ tablespoon rice flour	*Wheat free*
(optional – will make the oopsies	**Serves**
more bread like)	*2-4*

Oopsies are extremely versatile and a great alternative to bread rolls. Once cooked, they can be used as a gluten free hotdog or hamburger bun or as a base for some whipped cream and berries (leave out the rice flour for non-savoury options).

Method

1 Preheat oven to 150° C, 300° F, Gas 2.

2 Separate the eggs whites in one bowl and yolks in another.

3 Whisk the egg whites together with the salt until they are very stiff.

4 Mix the egg yolks and the cream cheese and then stir in the rice flour.

5 Tip the egg whites into the yolk mix and fold the two mixtures together.

6 Divide into 6 to 8 oopsies on a baking tray and bake for about 25 minutes, until a golden colour.

TIP *If you're in Phase 3, try mixing in a handful of mixed seeds before cooking to give a crunchier texture.*

Spicy chick pea patties (v)

Ingredients

225g (8oz) tin chick peas, drained and rinsed

25g (1oz) butter

1 medium onion, finely chopped

1 teaspoon ground cumin

1 teaspoon paprika

450g (1lb) tomatoes, finely chopped

100g (3.5oz) Cheddar cheese, grated

Sea salt and pepper

Suitable for

Phase 3 (mix) (Always better to mix with real food than cheat with fake food)

Candida

Hypoglycemia

Wheat free

Serves

2-4

Method

1 Put half the chick peas in a bowl and blend with a hand blender, using a little water, if needed.

2 Melt the butter in a frying pan and lightly cook the onion for 5 minutes, until transparent. Then stir in the cumin and paprika and the remaining chick peas and cook for a further 2 minutes, stirring frequently. Add the tomatoes and blended chick peas.

3 Reduce the heat and simmer for 10 minutes to thicken the mixture.

4 Remove from the heat and stir in the cheese and season to taste and allow to cool. Then take a handful of the mixture and make into a small pattie and repeat until all the mixture is used up.

5 Lightly fry the patties on both sides in a little butter until lightly browned. Then chill and use as required.

Wheat-free flans (v)

Ingredients	Suitable for
150g (5oz) white rice flour	Phase 3 (mix)
1 teaspoon rosemary, chopped	Candida
1 teaspoon sea salt	Hypoglycemia
100g (3.5oz) butter, chilled and cut into small pieces	Wheat free
	Serves
50ml (2oz) cold water	4-6
2 tablespoons butter or olive oil	
For the Topping:	
2 teaspoons butter	
1 large onion, peeled and finely sliced	
75g (2.5oz) Emmental cheese, sliced	
2 large tomatoes, sliced	

Like Frittatas, flans are endlessly versatile dishes and this delicious wheat free version means that you can enjoy it without having those wheat belly moments.

Method

1 In a bowl, mix the white rice flour, rosemary and salt.

2 Add the butter and mix with a fork until no large pieces of butter remain. The mixture should now look like a crumble. Add the water and continue mixing until you have a doughy mixture.

3 Lightly grease a flan dish and, one-tablespoon piece of dough at a time, press into the bottom of the flan dish, covering the dish evenly. Lightly cover the dish with plastic wrap and freeze for 30 minutes.

4 Preheat the oven to 190° C, 375° F, Gas 5.

5 For the topping: Melt the butter in a frying pan and add the onion and fry for about 20 minutes until lightly brown. Stir frequently.

6 Remove the base from the freezer and cover the top with butter or oil. Pop in the oven and bake the base for about 30 minutes, until lightly brown. Remove from the oven

7 Cover the flan base with the sliced Emmental and spoon the onions evenly over cheese. Finish with the sliced tomatoes. Drizzle lightly with olive oil.

8 Increase the oven temperature to 220° C, 425° F, Gas 7 and bake for a further 20 minutes until the tomatoes soften. Remove from the oven and allow to cool on a wire rack.

9 Serve as required.

TIP *Why not try some of these alternatives toppings, or create your own favourite: Courgette, pepper & Mozzarella; Roasted tomatoes & Feta; Asparagus & Cheddar cheese.*

Courgette, pepper & Mozzarella

Ingredients	Suitable for
1 buffalo Mozzarella, sliced	Phase 2 (fat) for this topping
1 courgette, finely sliced	Candida
1 red pepper, finely sliced	Hypoglycemia
	Wheat free

Method

1 Slice the Mozzarella thin enough so that the slices completely cover the flan base (recipe p. 63).

2 Arrange the courgette and red pepper slices over the Mozzarella so that they evenly cover the base.

3 Cook in the oven at 200° C, 400° F, Gas 6 for a further 30 minutes.

Roasted Tomatoes & Feta

Ingredients	Suitable for
4 large tomatoes, quartered	Phase 2 (fat) for this topping
2 tablespoons olive oil	Candida
100g (2oz) feta cheese, crumbled	Hypoglycemia
	Wheat free

Method

1 Place the quartered tomatoes on a baking tray and drizzle over the olive oil. Pop in a preheated oven at 200° C, 400° F, Gas 6 for 30 minutes, until the tomatoes start to brown.

2 Sprinkle the crumbled feta over the flan base (recipe p. 63) and then evenly cover with the roasted tomatoes, making an attractive pattern

3 Cook in the oven at 200° C, 400° F, Gas 6 for a further 30 minutes.

TIP *For a spicier alternative, replace the roasted tomatoes with some chilli roast tomatoes (p. 80).*

Asparagus & Cheddar cheese

Ingredients	Suitable for
300g (10.5oz) asparagus	Phase 2 (fat) for this topping
2 eggs	Candida
50g (2oz) cheddar cheese, grated	Hypoglycemia
200ml (7oz) double cream	Wheat free
Sea salt and freshly ground pepper	

Method

1 Remove the woody end of the asparagus and drop the tips into boiling water and cook for 3 minutes. Drain and rinse with cold water. Then chop them into 3cm, lengths and arrange onto the flan base (recipe p. 63).

2 Whisk the eggs in a mixing bowl and stir in the cream and cheddar. Season well and then pour the mixture over the asparagus.

3 Cook in the oven at 200° C, 400° F, Gas 6 for a further 30 minutes.

TIP *The toppings suggested for the wheat free flan base can also be used as topping options on our Lunchbox Eggza (p. 51).*

Lentil & buckwheat biscuits (v)

Ingredients	Suitable for
100g (3.5oz) buckwheat	Phase 2 (carb)
2 tablespoons olive oil	Candida
1 onion, finely chopped	Hypoglycemia
1 carrot, grated	Wheat free (despite the name,
175g (6oz) red lentils	buckwheat is not wheat)
1 litre (1.5pints) vegetable stock	**Serves**
2 teaspoons chopped parsley	4-6
Sea salt and pepper	

Method

1 Preheat the oven to 200° C, 400° F, Gas 6.

2 Under a hot grill, toast the dry buckwheat grains for about 5 minutes until golden brown.

3 Heat the oil in a frying pan and lightly fry the onion and carrot for about 5 minutes until the onion is transparent.

4 Add the toasted buckwheat, along with all the other ingredients, and pour the stock into the pan. Bring quickly to the boil and then reduce and simmer for about 30 minutes until all the liquid is absorbed by the ingredients.

5 Press the mixture into a greased baking dish and score with a knife to make biscuit sized chunks. Bake for 30 minutes until the top is nicely brown.

6 Allow to cool then turn out onto a plate and break into 'biscuits' along the score lines.

Lentil & cheese slab (v)

Ingredients	Suitable for
225g (8oz) red lentils	Phase 3 (mix)
450ml (1pint) water	Candida
1 large onion, finely chopped	Hypoglycemia
25g (1oz) butter	Wheat free
100g (3.5oz) cheddar cheese, grated	**Serves**
1 teaspoon dried mixed herbs	4
1 egg, beaten	
1 tablespoon rice flour (optional)	
Salt and pepper to season	

Like the spicy chick pea patties this does mix pulses and cheese, but these are great options for vegetarians for a healthy and filling lunch. Mix cheating is always better than sandwiches.

Method

1 Preheat the oven to 200° C, 400° F, Gas 6.

2 Put the lentils and water in a saucepan, bring to the boil, then reduce and simmer for about 30 minutes, until the lentils are soft. Drain and transfer to a mixing bowl.

3 Fry the onion with the butter for about 5 minutes until transparent, then add this to the lentils.

4 Add all the other ingredients to the mixing bowl and mix thoroughly. Then press the mixture into a greased flan dish or sandwich tin and bake in a moderate-hot oven 200° C, 400° F, Gas 6 for 30 minutes, or until the top is nicely brown.

5 Allow to cool then transfer to a plate, if using a flan dish, or slice from the sandwich tin.

Carrot, parsnip, celeriac & mixed seed bake (v)

Ingredients

1kg (2lb) total weight of grated
carrot, parsnip and celeriac
– equal quantities

½ red onion, finely chopped

½ teaspoon chopped rosemary

100g (3.5oz) mixed seeds (pumpkin,
sunflower, sesame etc)

1 egg, beaten

1 tablespoon rice flour

freshly ground pepper and
generous pinch of sea salt

Suitable for

Phase 3 (mix)

Candida

Hypoglycemia (if you are very
carb sensitive, this quantity of root
vegetables may be best avoided)

Wheat free

Dairy free

Serves

4

This is a great alternative to nut roast - using seeds and root vegetables instead of nuts and rice.

Method

1 Preheat the oven to 175° C, 350° F, Gas 4

2 Put the grated carrot, parsnip and celeriac in a large mixing bowl along with the onion, rosemary and mixed seeds and mix thoroughly.

3 In a separate bowl, whisk the eggs and rice flour then pour over the mixture in the first bowl and mix thoroughly with a fork.

4 Spoon the mixture into a loaf dish (or shallow baking dish) and squeeze down so that the whole mixture is compacted.

5 Roast in the oven for about 40 minutes, until the top starts to brown.

Chewy fruit bars (v)

Ingredients

100g (3.5oz) dried apricots, chopped

100ml (3.5oz) orange juice

1 teaspoon orange rind, grated

50g (2oz) desiccated coconut

50g (2oz) mixed nuts, chopped

100g (3.5oz) ground almonds

50g (2oz) dried fruit

50g (2oz) puffed rice cereal

Suitable for

Phase 3 (mix)

Candida

Wheat free

Serves

10-12

Due to the high level of fruit and nuts, these bars are not strictly 'Harcombe friendly'. However, when compared to other cereal bar alternatives, these are a much better option for busy people on the go. If you're a sales rep, for example, and you really can't store meat and salads safely in the car 'till lunch time, these bars are far better than the meal deal at the service stations.

Method

1 Put the apricots, orange juice and rind in a small pan, quickly bring to the boil then reduce and simmer for 5 minutes.

2 Put the desiccated coconut and chopped nuts on a baking tray and lightly toast for 2-3 minutes until they start to lightly brown.

3 Put the ground almonds, dried fruit and puffed rice cereal in a mixing bowl and blitz for a few seconds with a hand blender. Then stir in all the other ingredients.

4 Pour the ingredients into a lightly greased shallow biscuit tin, pressing the mixture down flat. Cut them into equal sized 'bars', probably around a dozen, then leave on a cooling rack to dry out and solidify.

Nut roast (v)

Ingredients

175g (6oz) brown rice (dry weight)

600ml (21oz) of vegetable stock

2 small onions, finely chopped

1 clove garlic, finely chopped

4 mushrooms, finely chopped

1 stick celery, finely chopped

2 tablespoons olive oil

175g (6oz) mixed nuts, chopped
(hazelnuts, cashews, almonds &
brazils work really well)

1 sprig fresh rosemary

1 sprig fresh thyme
(or ½ teaspoon of each herb
dried if you can't get fresh)

Salt & ground black pepper

1 egg (optional)

1 apple, (cooking or eating)

Suitable for

Phase 3 (mix)

Candida

Hypoglycemia

Wheat free

Dairy free

Serves

4-6

Strictly a Phase 3 dish, as it mixes fats and carbs in reasonable quantities, but this is a very satiating loaf to keep hunger at bay when you're out and about.

Method

1 Preheat the oven to 200° C, 400° F, Gas 6.

2 Part cook the brown rice in the vegetable stock (cook for half the recommended time).

3 Drain the rice through a sieve and put it in a mixing bowl and leave it to one side.

4 Stir-fry the vegetables in the olive oil. Then add them to the rice.

5 Add the chopped nuts to the mixing bowl with the rice & vegetables.

6 Add in the rosemary, thyme, salt & pepper.

7 Crack the egg into a small bowl and beat with a fork until mixed in.

8 Add the egg to everything else (without the egg the mixture doesn't bind and will be crumbly but this doesn't affect the taste).

9 Put half the mixture into a loaf (glass) oven dish and press it down well into the dish.

10 Core & slice the apple on top of the mixture until it makes an apple layer. Put the rest of the mixture on top (pressing it down well again) so that you have made an apple sandwich.

11 Cover the loaf dish with tin foil.

12 Bake for 30-45 minutes, or until the top of the roast is golden.

TIP 1 *Substitute peppers for the mushrooms, or just leave out the mushrooms, for this dish to be suitable for Candida.*

TIP 2 *This is perfect for vegetarians to bake at the weekend and then five lunches are sorted – just vary the salads and dips.*

Chapter 5

Salads

There is a lot more to salads than a few wilted lettuce leaves that you used to get as garnish with your pub meal. With a little creativity, salads can make any lunch an exciting and exotic mix of flavours, packed with nutrients to help keep you alert through to your next meal. We've listed some of our favourites, which can be made and stored usually for up to five days at any time of the year (check the use-by date, but always do the 'sniff & taste' test).

In this chapter:

- *Coleslaw with yoghurt (v)*
- *Celery & apple with yoghurt (v)*
- *Chilli roast tomatoes (v)*
- *Waldorf salad (v)*
- *Creamy beetroot salad (v)*
- *Watercress & beetroot salad (v)*
- *Watercress & tomato salad (v)*
- *Mixed leaf salad (v)*
- *Greek salad (v)*
- *Mixed pepper & red onion salad (v)*
- *Beetroot with fresh mint (v)*
- *Tomato, bean & basil salad (v)*
- *Herb grilled tomatoes (v)*
- *Citrus salad (v)*
- *Pear & blue cheese salad (v)*
- *Butternut squash wedges (v)*

Coleslaw with yoghurt (v)

Ingredients*	Suitable for
250g (9oz) Natural live yoghurt (NLY)	Phase 2 (fat)
1 large teaspoon of Dijon mustard	Candida
Freshly ground pepper	Hypoglycemia
Big pinch of sea salt	Wheat free
½ red onion, finely chopped.	Note: For a red cabbage free version (low FODMAP* alternative), replace the vegetables as follows:
1 large carrot, grated,	1 red onion, finely chopped.
¼ celeriac, grated and equal in volume to the large carrot	2 large carrots, grated,
¼ red cabbage, finely chopped	½ celeriac, grated and equal in volume to the large carrot

Method

1 Put the NLY, mustard, salt and pepper in a large mixing bowl and stir to a smooth consistency.

2 Add all the chopped and grated vegetables and stir well.

3 Serve as desired.

* FODMAPs stands for Fermentable, Oligo-, Di-, Mono-saccharides and Polyols. They comprise fructose, lactose, fructo- and galacto-oligosaccharides (fructans and galactans), and polyols (such as sorbitol, mannitol, xylitol and maltitol) that are poorly absorbed in the small intestine. People aware of FODMAPS avoid some foods because it helps with Irritable Bowel Syndrome and tummy discomfort.

Celery & apple with yoghurt (v)

Ingredients	Suitable for
250g (9oz) low-fat Natural Live Yoghurt (NLY)	Phase 2 (carb)
Juice of half a lemon	Candida
Big pinch of sea salt	Hypoglycemia
Freshly ground pepper	Wheat free
2 large apples, cored and thinly sliced	
4 sticks of celery, finely chopped.	

If you're in Phase 3, or don't worry about a healthy mix, this is tastier with normal (full fat) Natural Live Yoghurt. However, we've advised low-fat NLY here because the apples make this a carb meal.

In 2 large apples there are approximately 60g of carbohydrate, of which almost 50g is sugar (the rest being fibre). A handy reminder of just how sugary fruit is. Do try this recipe though - it's a meal in itself.

Method

1 Put the NLY, lemon juice, salt and pepper in a large mixing bowl and stir to a smooth consistency.

2 Add all the sliced apple and chopped celery and stir well.

3 Serve as desired.

Chilli roast tomatoes (v)

Ingredients

400g (14oz) cherry tomatoes

4 tablespoons olive oil

1-2 teaspoons chilli flakes

Suitable for

Phase 1 & 2 (can accompany a carb/fat meal)

Candida

Hypoglycemia

Wheat free

Dairy free

Method

1 Preheat the oven to 175° C, 350° F, Gas 4.

2 Put the tomatoes in a roasting dish and drizzle the olive oil over them.

3 Sprinkle the chilli flakes over the tomatoes and pop in the pre-heated oven and roast for 30 minutes, until the tomatoes start to brown.

4 Chill and serve as required.

TIP *The oil mixed with the tomato juices is sweet and hot and is a deliciously simple dressing for a green salad.*

Waldorf salad (v)

Ingredients	Suitable for
4 celery sticks, finely sliced	Phase 2 (fat)
50g (2oz) walnuts	Candida (if the mayonnaise is replaced with NLY)
1 red pepper, deseeded and diced	
150g (5oz) mayonnaise (see recipe p. 107)	Hypoglycemia
	Wheat free
Sea salt and freshly ground pepper	Dairy free (if mayo, not NLY)

The classic Waldorf salad has celery, apple, nuts and mayonnaise. This would be a mix with the carb of the apple, the fat of the mayo and the natural mix of the nuts. To lessen the mix, we go for red pepper instead of the apple. It's just as crunchy and colourful, but we now have a mostly fat meal, with just a dash of nut mixing.

Method

1 Put all the ingredients into a large mixing bowl and mix thoroughly.

2 Chill and serve as required.

3 Options

4 Replace the mayonnaise with Natural Live Yoghurt (NLY) for a tangier option and to avoid the vinegar in the mayo if you're very Candida sensitive.

5 Add a couple of diced dried apricots for a bit of sweetness and a bit of mixing if desired.

Creamy beetroot salad (v)

Ingredients

250g (9oz) beetroot, grated

250g (9oz) parsnips, grated

3 teaspoons chopped parsley

150g (5oz) Natural Live Yoghurt

2 tablespoons cider or
white wine vinegar

Sea salt and freshly ground pepper

Suitable for

Phase 1 (can be) & Phase 2 (fat)

Candida (without the vinegar)

Hypoglycaemia

Wheat free

Method

1 Add the grated beetroot and parsnips to a large mixing bowl and then add all the other ingredients and mix thoroughly.

2 Chill and serve as required.

3 Options

4 Replace the parsnips with carrots.

5 Leave out the vinegar for a great Phase 1 coleslaw alternative.

Watercress & beetroot salad (v)

Ingredients	Suitable for
100g (3.5oz) watercress, roughly chopped	Phase 1 & 2 (can accompany a carb/fat meal)
4 medium beetroot, cooked, peeled and quartered	Candida
2 tablespoons extra virgin olive oil	Hypoglycaemia
Sea salt and freshly ground pepper	Wheat free
	Dairy free

Method

1 Mix the watercress and beetroot in a bowl and then pour over the olive oil.

2 Season and serve as required.

Watercress & tomato salad (v)

Ingredients

100g (3.5oz) watercress, roughly chopped

¼ cucumber, diced

250g (9oz) tomatoes, diced

3 teaspoons fresh mint, chopped

2 tablespoons olive oil or classic French dressing (see p. 108)

Sea salt and freshly ground pepper

Suitable for

Phase 1 (can be) & Phase 2 (can accompany a carb/fat meal)

Candida (with olive oil, not the French dressing)

Hypoglycaemia

Wheat free

Dairy free

Method

1 Mix all the salad ingredients in a bowl and then toss with sufficient dressing to cover the salad.

2 Season and serve as required.

TIP *Choose the olive oil option to be suitable for Phase 1.*

Mixed leaf salad (v)

Ingredients	Suitable for
Approximately 400g (14oz) of mixed leaves – e.g. Cos, Romaine, little gems, round head, radicchio, spinach, rocket, watercress etc	Phase 1 (can be) & Phase 2 (can accompany a carb/fat meal)
2 tablespoons olive oil or classic French dressing (p. 108)	Candida (with olive oil, not the French dressing)
Sea salt and freshly ground pepper	Hypoglycaemia
	Wheat free
	Dairy free

This is hardly a recipe, more a reminder that, sometimes, the simplest of dishes are the tastiest and should not be forgotten. You can get pre-packed bags of mixed leaves from the supermarket, which are pre-washed (bleached) or you can make your own from simple leaves (much tastier and far more nutritious).

Method

1 Rinse the leaves in cold running water and spin dry in a salad spinner. Chop up all the various leaves into roughly the same size pieces and put in a large mixing bowl.

2 Drizzle over the olive oil or French dressing and toss the leaves until they are all nicely covered by the oil/dressing.

3 Serve as desired.

TIP 1 Choose the olive oil option to be suitable for Phase 1.

TIP 2 This is absolutely delicious topped with the Celery & apple with yoghurt salad (p. 78).

Greek salad (v)

Ingredients

200g (7oz) iceberg lettuce, shredded or chopped

75g (2.5oz) cucumber, diced

4 medium tomatoes, diced

1 small red onion, thinly sliced

150g (6oz) feta cheese

1 tablespoon freshly chopped basil

50ml (2oz) classic French dressing (p. 108)

Sea salt and freshly ground pepper

Suitable for

Phase 2 (fat)

Candida (can be)

Hypoglycaemia

Wheat free

Method

1 Add all the ingredients to a large mixing bowl and toss until the leaves are well covered with dressing.

2 Season to taste and serve as required.

TIP *Use olive oil instead of French dressing to be suitable for Candida.*

Mixed pepper & red onion salad (v)

Ingredients

50g (2oz) olive oil

2 cloves garlic, thinly sliced

1 each large red, yellow & green pepper, deseeded and sliced

1 red onion, thinly sliced

1 tablespoon white wine vinegar

Sea salt and freshly ground pepper

Suitable for

Phase 1 (can be) & Phase 2 (can accompany a carb/fat meal)

Candida (without the vinegar)

Hypoglycaemia

Wheat free

Dairy free

Method

1 Heat the oil in a frying pan and add the garlic, fry for about a minute until it just turns brown.

2 Reduce the heat, add the peppers and onion and cook for about 10 minutes, stirring frequently, until they just begin to soften.

3 Transfer the mixture to a mixing bowl, pour over the white wine vinegar and give the whole lot a good stir.

4 Season, chill and serve as required.

TIP *Leave out the vinegar for Phase 1.*

Beetroot with fresh mint (v)

Ingredients

6 medium beetroot, cooked, sliced or diced

2 tablespoons balsamic vinegar

Handful of fresh mint, chopped

2 tablespoons olive oil

Sea salt and freshly ground pepper

Suitable for

Phase 2 (can accompany a carb/fat meal)

Candida (without the vinegar)

Hypoglycaemia

Wheat free

Dairy free

Method

1 Add all the ingredients to a large mixing bowl and mix thoroughly with a fork until the ingredients are well mixed together.

2 Chill and use as required.

Tomato, bean & basil salad (v)

Ingredients

5 tablespoons olive oil

15g (1/2oz) fresh basil or coriander leaves, roughly chopped

300g (10.5oz) cherry tomatoes, halved

400g (14oz) tin of mixed beans, drained and rinsed

Sea salt and freshly ground pepper

Suitable for

Phase 2 (carb)

Candida

Hypoglycaemia

Wheat free

Dairy free

Method

1 Heat the olive oil in a pan and lightly fry the basil leaves for about a minute, until they start to change colour.

2 Add all the ingredients to a large mixing bowl and mix thoroughly with a fork until the ingredients are well mixed together.

3 Chill and use as required.

Herb grilled tomatoes (v)

Ingredients	Suitable for
6 medium tomatoes	Phase 1 & 2 (can accompany a
2 teaspoons dried mixed herbs	carb/fat meal)
25g (1oz) butter	Candida
	Hypoglycaemia
	Wheat free

Dr Kaayla Daniel calls vegetables "a delivery mechanism for butter"! This recipe certainly is.

These are equally delicious hot or cold – make plenty – some for the lunch box and some to fry with eggs for breakfast.

Method

1 Chop the top off the tomatoes and gently slash the flesh with a small sharp knife.

2 Sprinkle each tomato with dried mixed herbs and top with a small knob of butter.

3 Grill under a medium grill until the butter melts and the herbs start to brown.

Citrus salad (v)

Ingredients

2 oranges, peeled, pith removed and cut into segments

4 spring onions, chopped

225g (8oz) sweetcorn

100g (3.5oz) cashew, walnut or mixed nuts

1 teaspoon sesame seeds (roasted if time permits)

1 teaspoon ground ginger

1 teaspoon Tamari soya sauce

50ml (2oz) French dressing or olive oil

Sea salt and freshly ground pepper

Suitable for

Phase 3 (mix)

Candida (can be)

Hypoglycaemia

Wheat free

Dairy free

Method

1 Add all the ingredients to a large mixing bowl and toss until the leaves are well covered with dressing.

2 Season to taste and serve as required

TIP Use olive oil instead of French dressing to be suitable for Candida.

Pear & blue cheese salad (v)

Ingredients	Suitable for
4 pears, quartered and cored	Phase 3 (mix)
100g (3.5oz) blue cheese	Hypoglycaemia
dressing/dip (p. 113)	Wheat free
1 tablespoon balsamic vinegar	
3 tablespoons olive oil	

This can double as a dinner party starter, as well as a 5* lunch box option. It's a mix because of the fruit with the cheese dressing. We think of pears as a lower sugar fruit, but a small pear still has 23g of carbohydrate, of which approximately 15g is sugar. This really is a meal in itself, however, even though it's in the salad section.

Method

1 Place the pears in a mixing bowl and spoon over the blue cheese dressing and mix until the pears are nicely covered by the dressing.

2 Mix the olive oil and vinegar together in a cup and then drizzle over the pear and blue cheese.

3 Chill and use as required

Butternut squash wedges (v)

Ingredients	Suitable for
1 butternut squash, quartered and deseeded	Phase 1 & 2 (can accompany a carb/fat meal)
3 tablespoons olive oil	Candida
1 tablespoon fresh herbs, finely chopped	Hypoglycaemia
	Wheat free
	Dairy free

Method

1 Preheat the oven to 200° C, 400° F, Gas 6.

2 Place the butternut squash quarters on a roasting dish and drizzle the olive oil over them. Roast in a preheated oven for 30 minutes then remove from the oven.

3 Sprinkle the squash with the herbs and pop back in the oven for a further 15 minutes until the flesh is soft and the edges begin to brown.

4 Chill and use as required.

5 These wedges are delicious on their own, topped with raw tomato salsa (p. 102) and a green salad.

Chapter 6

Sauces & Dips

Sauces and dips are great with crudités as an appetiser at dinner parties and they also give a fantastic boost to any packed lunch. We've taken some classic dips and made them 'Harcombe friendly' and have included a few others that we've created or come across on our travels. We usually make a few in advance, so that we have some variety throughout the week.

In this chapter:

- *Raw tomato salsa (v)*
- *Lanzarote mojo sauces (v)*
- *Yoghurt dips & sauces (v)*
- *Basic mayonnaise (v)*
- *Classic French dressing (v)*
- *Aioli (v)*
- *Hummus (v)*
- *Guacamole (v)*
- *Blue cheese dressing/dip (v)*
- *Infused oils (v)*
- *Yellow pepper & coriander relish (v)*

Raw tomato salsa (v)

Ingredients

450g (1lb) ripe tomatoes

A few healthy dashes of Tabasco sauce

1 tablespoon wine vinegar

1 clove garlic, crushed

½ red onion, finely chopped

Sea salt and freshly ground pepper

2 tablespoons fresh basil, chopped

100g (3.5oz) olive oil

Suitable for

Phase 2 (can accompany a carb/fat meal)

Candida (without the vinegar)

Hypoglycaemia

Wheat free

Dairy free

There's nothing quite like a good tomato relish to add to cold meats and this one is so simple, there's no excuse for not always having a small pot in the fridge

Method

1 Liquidise the tomatoes with a food processor or blender and then add all the other ingredients. Whisk with a fork and serve as a side relish.

Lanzarote mojo sauces (v)

Red version

Ingredients	Suitable for
2 large, sweet red peppers, deseeded and sliced	Phase 1 & 2 (can accompany a carb/fat meal)
5-8, fresh red chillies, deseeded and sliced	Candida
	Hypoglycemia
50g (2oz) olive oil	Wheat free
Juice of 1 lemon	Dairy free
Sea salt	

We love the Canaries and have visited Lanzarote on a number of occasions. The climate is delightful and the food is deliciously fresh and simple. These sauces are served at most meal and you'll understand why, as they add a burst of taste and colour to just about any dish.

Method

1 Cook the peppers and chillies in a little salted water for 3-4 minutes, until they start to soften.

2 Drain and puree the pepper and chilli in a blender, then stir in the olive oil and lemon juice.

3 Mix in a good pinch of sea salt and chill.

4 Will keep up to a week in a fridge.

Green version

Ingredients

3 cloves garlic, chopped

Sea salt

1 teaspoon cumin, ground

2 green peppers, deseeded and chopped

Handful of fresh coriander or parsley, chopped

10ml (½oz) white wine vinegar

50g (2oz) olive oil

Suitable for

Phase 2 (can accompany a carb/fat meal)

Hypoglycemia

Wheat free

Dairy free

Method

1 Place the chopped garlic into a mixing bowl and crush it with some sea salt.

2 Transfer the garlic to a food processor and add the cumin, chopped peppers, coriander and white wine vinegar. Then, blitz for a few seconds until you get a smooth paste. Then, scoop out the mixture back to the mixing bowl.

3 Finally, slowly pour in the olive oil, whisking as you add it, until you have a lovely smooth green sauce.

Yoghurt dips & sauces (v)

Ingredients	Suitable for
250g (9oz) Natural Live Yoghurt	Phase 1 & 2 (fat)
Handful of fresh mint, chopped	Candida
Sea salt and freshly ground pepper	Hypoglycaemia
	Wheat free

Natural Live Yoghurt (NLY) makes a wonderful base for a sauce, dip or salad dressing. Our first one uses fresh mint, which gives a deliciously fresh taste. If you like this one, try some of the other suggestions below.

Method

1 Put all the ingredients in a mixing bowl and mix thoroughly.

2 Chill for a few hours and then use as required.

TIP *This will keep up to five days in an airtight container in a fridge and the longer you keep it, the stronger the mint flavour.*

Variations (replace the mint with):

1 2 teaspoons of paprika; Or

2 Lots of freshly ground black pepper; Or

3 The juice of 2 fresh chilli's, crushed with a garlic crusher; Or

4 Handful of fresh coriander or basil, chopped; Or

5 ¼ cucumber, deseeded and chopped into small chunks.

Basic mayonnaise (v)

Ingredients	Suitable for
2 eggs, at room temperature	Phase 2 (fat)
Juice of half a lemon	Hypoglycaemia
1 tablespoon wine vinegar	Wheat free
Sea salt and pepper	Dairy free
200ml (7oz) extra virgin olive oil	

Method

1 Break the eggs into a food processor and add all the other ingredients, except the oil.

2 Blend on high for about 30 seconds until the eggs are foaming. Turn the speed down to half and pour in the oil slowly and evenly until you end up with a consistent paste.

3 Will keep up to 5 days in an airtight container in a fridge.

Classic French dressing (v)

Ingredients	Suitable for
3 tablespoons white wine vinegar	Phase 2 (fat)
2 teaspoons Dijon mustard	Hypoglycaemia
5 tablespoons olive oil	Wheat free
Sea salt and freshly ground black pepper	Dairy free

Method

1 Put the white wine vinegar and Dijon mustard in a bowl or mug, and whisk with a fork until completely combined.

2 Slowly add the olive oil, whisking all the time, until you have a smooth emulsion.

3 Season well with sea salt and pepper.

TIP 1 *This dressing should have quite a bite to it, but if it's too mild for your taste, add some more mustard or vinegar.*

TIP 2 *This recipe also works with other mustards and vinegars. Try sherry or cider vinegar and wholegrain mustard.*

Aioli (v)

Ingredients	Suitable for
4 cloves garlic	*Phase 1 & 2 (fat)*
1 egg yolk	*Hypoglycaemia*
100g (3.5oz) olive oil	*Wheat free*
Juice of half a lemon	*Dairy free*
Sea salt and freshly ground pepper	

Method

1 Put all the ingredients, except the olive oil, into a food processor, turn on, blend for a few seconds and then slowly pour in the oil until you have a beautiful, thick sauce.

Hummus (v)

Ingredients

250g (9oz) tin of chickpeas, drained and rinsed

1 clove garlic, finely chopped

Juice of half a lemon

2 tablespoons olive oil

4 tablespoons low-fat NLY

Sea salt and freshly ground pepper

Chopped parsley to garnish (optional)

Suitable for

Phase 2 (carb)

Candida

Hypoglycaemia

Wheat free

Go for low-fat Natural Live Yoghurt (NLY) if you want to avoid mixing. Enjoy the regular NLY if you're fine with a bit of mixing. This makes a perfect vegetarian carb lunch with a couple of oat biscuits.

Method

1 Drain the tinned chickpeas and place them in a saucepan. Cover with water, bring to the boil and then simmer for about 20 minutes until they soften. Then drain and allow to cool.

2 Put the oil, lemon juice, garlic, yoghurt and chick peas into a mixing bowl and give them a few quick blasts with a hand blender (or put the ingredients in a food processor and blast for a few seconds).

3 Season with salt and pepper and give a final quick stir with a spoon.

4 Transfer to a dish and sprinkle with chopped parsley.

5 Chill and use as required.

Guacamole (v)

Ingredients	Suitable for
3 avocados	Phase 2/3 (fat)
Juice of 1 lemon/lime (lime is traditionally used with guacamole, but lemons are more easily available)	Candida
	Hypoglycaemia
	Wheat free
1 small shallot, finely diced	Dairy free
Sea salt and freshly ground pepper	

In a 100g portion of avocado there are 15g of fat and 9g of carbohydrate. Avocados are, therefore, higher in fat than carb but they are a bit of a mix food. Have them in moderation in Phase 2 and with a fat meal when you do have them.

Method

1 In a medium bowl, combine the diced shallot, salt, and lemon/lime juice. Set aside for 10 minutes.

2 Pit and peel the avocados. Take half of the flesh and mash it in a bowl with a fork.

3 Pour the lemon/lime mixture into the bowl and combine with the mashed avocado.

4 Dice the remainder of the avocado flesh into 3/4-inch cubes and gently incorporate into the mixture in the bowl.

5 Add freshly ground pepper and a good pinch of sea salt.

Blue cheese dressing/dip (v)

Ingredients

100g (3.5oz) butter, softened

100g (3.5oz) blue cheese like Roquefort

Freshly ground black pepper

1 tablespoon olive oil

Suitable for

Phase 2 (fat)

Hypoglycaemia

Wheat free

Method

1 Whisk the butter, cheese, olive oil and pepper into a smooth paste and use immediately.

2 This will keep in a fridge for a week but you will need to soften the dressing before use (else it will just be like a hard lump of cheese!)

Infused oils (v)

The principle here is simple. Take about 250ml olive oil and heat it gently in a saucepan with the chosen ingredients for 15-20 minutes. Allow to cool then strain the oil into a glass bottle with a small additional amount of the ingredient and leave it to infuse for 2-3 weeks. Then use as required as an alternative to plain olive oil. You'll be amazed at the difference this simple little change will make to your salads. Here are some of our favourites to get you started.

Rosemary

Heat the oil with a handful of rosemary twigs. Allow to cool, then transfer to a glass bottle. Add a few sprigs of rosemary and seal for 2-3 weeks then use as required. Delicious on all meats, meatzas, eggzas and flans.

Chilli

Heat 8-10 whole small fresh or dried chillies, different colours make the infusion more attractive. Allow to cool, then transfer to a glass bottle. Add a few fresh/dried chillies and seal for 2-3 weeks then use as required. This is great for adding a kick to your cooking and salads.

Peppercorns

Heat 2 tablespoons mixed peppercorns (the Bristol blend has different colours) with the oil, then allow to cool before transferring to a glass bottle. Add a few peppercorns to the bottle, then seal for 2-3 weeks. Delicious on all salad greens.

Yellow pepper & coriander relish (v)

Ingredients

2 tablespoons sesame oil for cooking

2 large yellow peppers, seeded and diced

½ medium red onion, very finely sliced

1 large red chilli, deseeded and thinly sliced

Handful fresh coriander, chopped

Sea salt

Suitable for

Phase 1 & 2 (can accompany a carb/fat meal)

Candida

Hypoglycaemia

Wheat free

Dairy free

Method

1 Heat the oil in a frying pan and lightly fry the peppers for about 5 minutes, until they start to turn brown.

2 Add the red onion and cook for a further minute.

3 Transfer the peppers to a mixing bowl and add the coriander, sliced chilli and salt.

4 Stir well with a fork then chill before use.

Chapter 7

What you can eat

We sometimes hear people say that eating real food is too restrictive for modern day living and that there is not enough variety. We find this quite ironic given how restrictive the typical modern human's diet really is, being made up of predominantly, wheat, corn and sugar.

If you ever thought eating real food would limit your food choices, here's a starter list to think about and try.

When you combine the range of cuts of meat available (our ancestors would have eaten ALL the animal, not just the posh- cuts) with vegetables, herbs, fruits and so many different cooking methods, you can see the range of dishes that are available to us when we eat real food.

When we think of the abundance of options open to us, we can celebrate what we can have and not miss the rubbish that we can't.

Meats:

Beef, Buffalo, Chicken, Duck, Goat, Goose, Grouse, Lamb, Pheasant, Pigeon, Pork, Quail, Rabbit, Turkey, Venison (Plus Alligator, Bison, Crocodile, Elk, Emu, Frog, Kangaroo, Moose, Ostrich, Snails and Squirrel if you're going to be really adventurous!)

Fish and Seafood:

Barracuda, Cod, Catfish, Char, Carp, Herring, Salmon, Trout, Grayling,

Shark, Barramundi, Bass, Sea-bass, Mackerel, Tuna, Whiting, Bream, Turbot, Halibut, Coley, Eel, Dab, Dorado, Grouper, Emperor, Perch, Flatfish, Flounder, Haddock, Hake, Halibut, John Dory, Kingfish, Lemon sole, Sole, Ling, Mahi-mahi, Monkfish, Mullet, Parrotfish, Perch, Pike, Plaice, Pollock, Red Snapper, Roach, Sardine, Snapper, Sole, Swordfish, Whitebait, Octopus, Squid, Lobster, Shrimp, Mussels, Clams (and dozens of other seafoods).

Vegetables:

Artichokes, Asparagus, Aubergine, Bamboo, Beetroot, Broccoli, Brussels sprouts, Burdock, Cabbage (many varieties), Carrots, Cauliflower, Celeriac, Celery, Chard, Chicory, Courgettes, Cress, Cucumbers, Dandelion nettles, Endive, Fennel, Garlic, Kale, Kohlrabi, Lamb's lettuce, Leeks, Lettuce, Okra, Olives, Onions, Parsnips, Peppers, Radish, Salsify, Scallions, Shallots, Sorrel, Spinach, Squash (dozens of varieties), Tomatoes, Water chestnuts.

Herbs & Spices:

Allspice, Anise, Basil (many varieties) Bay Leaf, Black Mustard, Caraway, Cardamom, Carob, Cayenne pepper, Celery seed, Chervil, Chicory, Chilli Pepper, Chives, Cinnamon, Clove, Coriander, Cumin, Curry, Dill, Elderflower, Fennel, Fenugreek, Garlic, Ginger, Horseradish, Jasmine Lavender, Lemongrass, Licorice, Mace, Marjoram, Mint, Mustard, Nutmeg, Oregano, Paprika, Parsley, Pepper, Peppermint, Rosemary, Saffron, Sage, Sorel, Spearmint, Star anise, Tarragon, Thyme, Turmeric, Vanilla, Wasabi, Watercress.

Fruits (in moderation):

Apple, Apricot, Avocado, Banana, Bilberry, Blackberry, Blackcurrant, Blueberry, Cherry, Damson, Date, Elderberry, Fig, Gooseberry, Grape, Grapefruit, Guava, Kiwi fruit, Kumquat, Lemon, Lime, Lychee, Mango, Melon (many kinds), Nectarine, Orange, Papaya, Peach, Pear, Pineapple, Pomegranate, Raspberry, Redcurrant, Satsuma, Star fruit, Strawberry.

The Harcombe Diet®

www.theharcombedietclub.com

Phase 1 Summary.

1) Eat real food. We have included many examples on the 'allowed' list below. Fish swim in the sea; fish fingers don't – you'll get the idea.

2) Eat three times a day. *Ideally* get into the habit of eating three (or two) main meals a day, with snacks only if you are genuinely hungry.

3) Eat as much as you need from the allowed list. Don't eat anything that is not on this list – no fruit, no other grains, no milk, no cheese etc.

Phase 1 Allowed List.

Vegetables & Salads. Alfalfa, Artichoke, Asparagus, Aubergine, Bamboo shoots, Bean sprouts, Beetroot, Broccoli, Brussels sprouts, Bok choy, Cabbage (any), Carrots, Cauliflower, Celeriac, Celery, Chicory, Chillies (any), Courgettes, Cucumber, Dandelion, Endive, Fennel , Garlic, Green beans, Kale, Leeks, Lettuce (any), Mange tout, Marrow, Mustard greens, Okra, Onions, Parsnip, Peas, Peppers (any), Pumpkin, Radish, Rocket, Salsify, Shallots, Sorrel, Spinach, Spring onions, Squashes, Swiss chard, Swede, Turnip, Watercress, Water chestnuts.

Herbs & Spices. Basil, Bay leaves, Caraway, Cardamom, Chervil, Chives, Cinnamon, Cloves, Coriander, Cumin, Dill, Ginger, Marjoram, Mint, Nutmeg, Oregano, Paprika, Parsley, Pepper, Rosemary, Saffron, Sage, Salt, Tarragon, Thyme, Turmeric.

White Fish. Cod, Haddock, Halibut, Plaice, Turbot, Whiting.

Seafood. Clams, Crab, Lobster, Mussels, Oysters, Prawns, Winkles.

Oily Fish. Anchovies, Mackerel, Pilchards, Salmon, Tuna, Trout.

White Meat & Birds. Chicken, Duck, Goose, Guinea Fowl, Pheasant, Quail, Rabbit, Turkey.

Red Meat. Bacon, Beef, Gammon, Ham, Lamb, Pork, Veal, Venison.

Other. Eggs, Natural Live (Bio) Yoghurt, Tofu.

Misc. Butter, Olives, Olive oil, Tomatoes.

Drinks. Water, Herbal teas, Decaf tea & coffee.

The only food limited in quantity is brown rice/quinoa/plain oats of which you can have 50g dry weight or 150g if you are vegetarian, per day.
If you are allergic or intolerant to any 'allowed' foods, clearly avoid these.

The Harcombe Diet®

www.theharcombedietclub.com

Phase 2 Summary.

1) Don't eat processed foods;

2) Don't eat fats and carbohydrates at the same meal;

3) Don't eat foods that cause your cravings.

Fat Meals

Any (unprocessed) Meat – Bacon, Beef, Chicken, Duck, Gammon, Goose, Guinea Fowl, Ham, Lamb, Pheasant, Pork, Quail, Rabbit, Turkey, Veal, Venison.

Any (unprocessed) Fish – Anchovies, Cod, Haddock, Halibut, Mackerel, Plaice, Pilchards, Salmon, Seafood, Trout, Tuna, Whiting etc Includes tinned fish in only oil, salt and/or water.

Eggs – Chicken, Duck etc.

Dairy Products – Cheese, Milk, Butter, Cream, Yoghurt (ideally Natural Live Yoghurt).

Carb Meals

All Fruit

Whole-grains – Brown rice, Brown pasta, Brown rice pasta, 100% Whole-wheat bread, Quinoa, Millet etc.

Whole-wheat Cereal – Porridge oats, Brown rice cereal, Shredded Wheat, Other sugar-free cereal.

Beans & Pulses – Lentils, Broad beans, Kidney beans, Chick peas etc.

Baked Potatoes in their skins.

Eat With Either a Fat or Carb Meal.

Vegetables & Salads – See Phase 1 allowed list.

Tofu/Quorn – Vegetarian protein alternatives.

Certain Fruits – Olives, Tomatoes & Berries.

Low-fat dairy products – Milk, Cottage cheese & Yoghurt.

Herbs & Spices – See Phase 1 allowed list.

Further information at:
www.theharcombedietclub.com

The Harcombe Diet® is a registered trademark of Zoë Harcombe

Index

A

Aioli 109

B

Bacon wrapped chicken 29

(Loaded) Bacon strips 54

Basic mayonnaise 107

(Creamy) Beetroot salad 82

Beetroot with fresh mint 91

Blue cheese dressing/dip 113

Butternut squash wedges 98

C

Cajun seasoning 32

Carrot, parsnip, celeriac & mixed seed bake 71

Celery & apple with yoghurt 78

Cheese & bacon muffins 56

Cheese topped chicken breast 31

Chewy fruit bars 72

Chicken breast stuffed with Guacamole 26

Chicken burgers 36

Chicken liver parfait 53

Chilli prawns 44

Chilli roast chicken 25

Chilli roast tomatoes 80

Citrus salad 96

Classic French dressing 108

Coleslaw with yoghurt 76

Coronation chicken wrap 33

Creamy beetroot salad 82

Cheese

Cheese topped chicken breast 31

Meatza toppings 47-49

Lunchbox 'Eggza' 51

Cheese & bacon muffins 56

Frittata 59

Oopsies 61

Wheat-free flans 63

Lentil & cheese slab 70

Greek salad 87

Pear & blue cheese salad 97

Blue cheese dressing/dip 113

Chicken

Roast Chicken 21

Lemon and garlic roast chicken 22

Herb crusted chicken 23

Mustard roast chicken 24

Chilli roast chicken 25

Chicken breast stuffed with Guacamole 26

Bacon wrapped chicken 29

Tandoori Chicken 30

Cheese topped chicken breast 31

Coronation chicken wrap 33

Kebabs (pork, chicken, beef) 34

Chicken burgers

E

Egg mayonnaise 57

Eggza (Lunchbox) 51

Eggs

Scotch Eggs 38

Meatzas 45

Cheese & bacon muffins 56

Frittata 59

Omelette strips 60

Oopsies 61

Asparagus & Cheddar

cheese flan 63

Lentil & cheese slab 70

Carrot, parsnip, celeriac & mixed seed bake 71

Nut roast 73

F

(Classic) French dressing 108

Frittata 59

(Chewy) Fruit bars 72

G

Greek salad 87

Guacamole 112

H

Harissa spiced koftas 42

Herb crusted chicken 23

Herb grilled tomatoes 94

Homemade pâté 52

Hummus 110

I

Infused oils 115

K

Kebabs (Pork, Chicken, Beef) 34

L

Lanzarote mojo sauces 103

Lemon and garlic roast chicken 22

Lentil & buckwheat biscuits 69

Lentil & cheese slab 70

Loaded bacon strips 54

M

Meatzas 45

Meatza toppings 47

Mixed leaf salad 86

Mixed pepper & red onion salad 89

Mustard Roast Chicken 24

Mustard roast ham 40

N

Nut roast 73

O

Omelette strips 60

Oopsies 61

(Infused) Oils 115

P

Pear & blue cheese salad 97

R

Raw tomato salsa 102

Roast chicken 21

S

Scotch eggs 38

Slow roast pork 37

Spicy chick pea patties 62

T

Tandoori chicken 30

Tomato, bean & basil salad 92

(Raw) Tomato salsa 102

W

Waldorf salad 81

Watercress & beetroot salad 83

Watercress & tomato salad 85

Wheat-free flans 63

Y

Yellow pepper & coriander relish 116

Yoghurt dips & sauces 106

Yoghurt

Tandoori chicken 30

Coronation chicken wrap 33

Chicken burgers 36

Egg mayonnaise 57

Coleslaw with yoghurt 76

Celery & apple with yoghurt 78

Creamy beetroot salad 82

Yoghurt dips 106

Hummus 110

Z

Zingy fish patties 41

Other books by Zoë Harcombe:

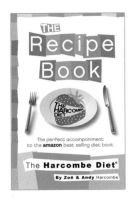

The Harcombe Diet:
The Recipe Book

Real food; great taste; optimal health – that's what The Harcombe Diet® is all about and here's how to do it. With over 100 recipes for Phase 1, another 100 for Phase 2 and some seriously special Phase 3 cheats, this is the ultimate diet-recipe book. If you want to eat well, lose weight and gain health – this is a must for your kitchen shelf.

ISBN 978-1-907797-07-1

The Harcombe Diet:
Stop Counting Calories
& Start Losing Weight

You've tried every diet under the sun. You've lost weight and put it back on. The more you diet, the more you crave food. You've given up hope of being slim. This book explains why. Count calories & end up a food addict. Stop Counting Calories& Start Losing Weight!

ISBN 978-1-907797-11-8

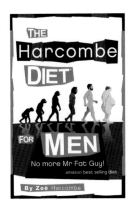

The Harcombe Diet for Men:
No More Mr Fat Guy

Men want to lose weight too - fast - and they won't go hungry. They want steak, pasta, cheese and the good things in life, including wine. They'll exercise if they want to; they won't count calories and they want all the answers in just a few pages...
So here it is - The Harcombe Diet® for men!

ISBN 978-1-907797-12-5

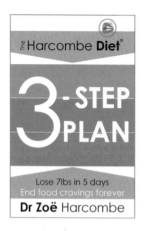

The Harcombe Diet
3-step plan

Zoë explains how dieting makes us fatter and introduces three common conditions, which cause uncontrollable food cravings. By following the 3-Step Plan you can overcome these conditions and lose weight - not by counting calories or starving yourself, but simply by eating real food.

ISBN 978-1-907797-00-2

Why do you overeat?
When all you want is to be slim

This book will explain Why do you overeat? when all you want is to be slim. It will tell you about the three common medical conditions, which are causing insatiable food cravings. It will give you the perfect diet to overcome these three conditions and so to end food addiction and overeating forever.

ISBN 978-1-907797-24-8

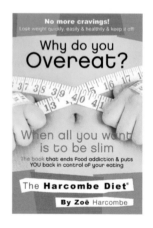

Find out more about
Zoë and/or The Harcombe Diet® at:

www.zoeharcombe.com
www.theharcombediet.com
www.theharcombedietclub.com

www.theharcombedietclub.com

Eat naturally, Move naturally
Lose weight, Gain health